LITERATURE & WRITING WORKSHOP

EXPLORING LYRIC POETRY

SCHOLASTIC INC.

ISBN 0-590-49304-3

CONTENTS

NATURE

Illustrated by
Ellen Joy Sasaki

In Quiet Night
Myra Cohn Livingston

In quiet night
the horns honking up from the street
make mad voices
to other horns, tires shriek
to other tires, brakes shriek
to other brakes.

Somewhere, there is a night of trees,
of great, bulging bullfrogs croaking
in ponds. Screech owls cry to a forest
of birds
         shrieking.

Horns, in quiet night, honk up songs
no frog, no bird, has ever sung.

April Rain Song

Langston Hughes

Let the rain kiss you.
Let the rain beat upon your head with silver liquid drops.
Let the rain sing you a lullaby.

The rain makes still pools on the sidewalk.
The rain makes running pools in the gutter.
The rain plays a little sleep-song on our roof at night—

And I love the rain.

April

Sara Teasdale

The roofs are shining from the rain,
   The sparrows twitter as they fly,
And with a windy April grace
   The little clouds go by.

Yet the backyards are bare and brown
   With only one unchanging tree—
I could not be so sure of Spring
   Save that it sings in me.

The Sea
James Reeves

The sea is a hungry dog,
Giant and grey.
He rolls on the beach all day.
With his clashing teeth and shaggy jaws
Hour upon hour he gnaws
The rumbling, tumbling stones,
And 'Bones, bones, bones, bones!'
The giant sea-dog moans,
Licking his greasy paws.

And when the night wind roars
And the moon rocks in the stormy cloud,
He bounds to his feet and snuffs and sniffs,
Shaking his wet sides over the cliffs,
And howls and hollos long and loud.

But on quiet days in May or June,
When even the grasses on the dune
Play no more their reedy tune,
With his head between his paws
He lies on the sandy shores,
So quiet, so quiet, he scarcely snores.

The Fall Of Plum Blossoms
Rankō

I came to look, and lo!
The plum tree petals scatter down,
A fall of purest snow.

Theme In Yellow
Carl Sandburg

I spot the hills
With yellow balls in autumn.
I light the prairie cornfields
Orange and tawny gold clusters
And I am called pumpkins.
On the last of October
When dusk is fallen
Children join hands
And circle round me
Singing ghost songs
And love to the harvest moon;
I am a jack-o'-lantern
With terrible teeth
And the children know
I am fooling.

The River Is A Piece Of Sky

John Ciardi

From the top of a bridge
The river below
Is a piece of sky—
    Until you throw
    a penny in
    Or a cockleshell
    Or a pebble or two
    Or a bicycle bell
    Or a cobblestone
    Or a fat man's cane—
And then you can see
It's a river again.

The difference you'll see
When you drop your penny:
The river has splashes,
The sky hasn't any.

The Hurricane

Pales Matos
Translated by Alida Malkus

When the hurricane unfolds
Its fierce accordion of winds,
On the tip of its toes,
Agile dancer, it sweeps whirling
Over the carpeted surface of the sea
With the scattered branches of the palm.

Silver

Walter de la Mare

Slowly, silently, now the moon
Walks the night in her silver shoon;
This way, and that, she peers, and sees
Silver fruit upon silver trees;
One by one the casements catch
Her beams beneath the silvery thatch;
Couched in his kennel, like a log,
With paws of silver sleeps the dog;
From their shadowy cote the white breasts peep
Of doves in a silver-feathered sleep;
A harvest mouse goes scampering by,
With silver claw, and silver eye;
And moveless fish in the water gleam,
By silver reeds in a silver stream.

The Rum Tum Tugger

T. S. *Eliot*

The Rum Tum Tugger is a Curious Cat:
If you offer him pheasant he would rather have grouse.
If you put him in a house he would much prefer a flat,
If you put him in a flat then he'd rather have a house.
If you set him on a mouse then he only wants a rat,   ~,.
If you set him on a rat then he'd rather chase a mouse.
Yes the Rum Tum Tugger is a Curious Cat—
   And there isn't any call for me to shout it:
      For he will do
      As he do do
         And there's no doing anything about it!

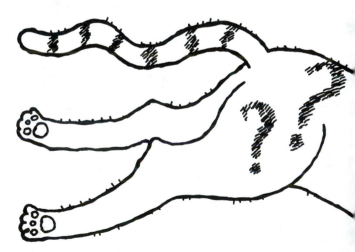

The Rum Tum Tugger is a terrible bore:
When you let him in, then he wants to be out;
He's always on the wrong side of every door,
As soon as he's at home, then he'd like to get about.
He likes to lie in the bureau drawer,
But he makes such a fuss if he can't get out.
Yes the Rum Tum Tugger is a Curious Cat—
   And it isn't any use for you to doubt it:
      For he will do
      As he do do
         And there's no doing anything about it!

The Rum Tum Tugger is a curious beast:
His disobliging ways are a matter of habit.
If you offer him fish then he always wants a feast;
When there isn't any fish then he won't eat rabbit.
If you offer him cream then he sniffs and sneers,
For he only likes what he finds for himself;
So you'll catch him in it right up to the ears,
If you put it away on the larder shelf.
The Rum Tum Tugger is artful and knowing,
The Rum Tum Tugger doesn't care for a cuddle;
But he'll leap on your lap in the middle of your sewing,
For there's nothing he enjoys like a horrible muddle.
Yes the Rum Tum Tugger is a Curious Cat—
   And there isn't any need for me to spout it:
      For he will do
      As he do do
         And there's no doing anything about it!

NATURE

The Grass
Emily Dickinson

The grass so little has to do,—
  A sphere of simple green,
With only butterflies to brood,
  And bees to entertain,

And stir all day to pretty tunes
  The breezes fetch along,
And hold the sunshine in its lap
  And bow to everything;

And thread the dews all night, like pearls,
  And make itself so fine,—
A duchess were too common
  For such a noticing.

And even when it dies, to pass
  In odours so divine,
As lowly spices gone to sleep,
  Or amulets of pine.

And then to dwell in sovereign barns,
  And dream the days away,—
The grass so little has to do,
  I wish I were the hay!

The Grass On The Mountain

From the Paiute American Indian
Transcribed by Mary Austin

Oh, long long
The snow has possessed the mountains.

The deer have come down and the big-horn,
They have followed the Sun to the south
To feed on the mesquite pods and the bunch grass.
Loud are the thunderdrums
In the tents of the mountains.
Oh, long long
Have we eaten chia seeds
And dried deer's flesh of the summer killing.
We are wearied of our huts
And the smoky smell of our garments.

We are sick with desire of the sun
And the grass on the mountain.

My Little Birds

A Jordanian Folk Poem
Translated by Henrietta Siksek-Su'ad

You have your water and your grain,
You have your fields all full of grass,
You have horizons far and wide.
Flutter along, my little birds.
Flutter along.... Flutter along....
And sing me a song, my little birds.

Come fly around me, little birds.
Do not fear a hunter's gun.
I am no hunter you can see.
Flutter along, my little birds.
Flutter along.... Flutter along.
And sing me a song, my little birds.

Your children are inside the nest,
Tucked in between feather and straw.
Your children will sleep undisturbed by me.
Flutter along, my little birds.
Flutter along.... Flutter along.
And sing me a song, my little birds.

Dancing

Yang Kuei-Fei
Translated by Florence Ayscough
and Amy Lowell

Wide sleeves sway.
Scents,
Sweet scents
Incessantly coming.

It is red lilies,
Lotus lilies,
Floating up,
And up,
Out of autumn mist.

Thin clouds
Puffed,
Fluttered,
Blown on a rippling wind
Through a mountain pass.

Young willow shoots
Touching,
Brushing
The water
Of the garden pool.

Give Me The Splendid Silent Sun

Walt Whitman

Give me the splendid silent sun with all its beams full-dazzling,
Give me juicy autumnal fruit ripe and red from the orchard,
Give me a field where the unmowed grass grows,
Give me an arbor, give me the trellised grape,
Give me fresh corn and wheat, give me serene-moving animals
    teaching content.
Give me nights perfectly quiet as on high plateaus west of the
    Mississippi, and I am looking up at the stars,
Give me odorous at sunrise a garden of beautiful flowers where I
    can walk undisturbed.

PEOPLE

Illustrated by
Tony DeLuna

Fisherman

Dionne Brand

He is dark and wiry,
his bones, thin and sharp,
like the bones of the fish
in his net.
It seems as if
webbing grows on his fingers
and feet,
a starfish is his heart,
a seagull is his voice,
an oyster's pearl his eye,
he juts out of the sand
like a rock or some coral,
so long he has lived in the sea.

Catherine

Karla Kuskin

Catherine said "I think I'll bake
A most delicious chocolate cake."
She took some mud and mixed it up
While adding water from a cup
And then some weeds and nuts and bark
And special gravel from the park
A thistle and a dash of sand.
She beat out all the lumps by hand.
And on the top she wrote "To You"
The way she says the bakers do
And then she signed it "Fondly C."
And gave the whole of it to me.
I thanked her but I wouldn't dream
Of eating cake without ice cream.

Big Brother

Elizabeth Madox Roberts

Our brother Clarence goes to school;
　He has a slate and a blue schoolbag.
He has a book and a copybook
　　And a scholar's companion and a little slate rag.

He knows a boy named Joe B. Kirk,
　And he learns about *c-a-t* cat,
And how to play one-two-sky-blue,
　And how to make a football out of a hat.

We climb up on the fence and gate
　And watch until he's small and dim,
Far up the street, and he looks back
　To see if we keep on watching him.

The Quarrel

Eleanor Farjeon

I quarreled with my brother,
I don't know what about,
One thing led to another
And somehow we fell out.
The start of it was slight,
The end of it was strong,
He said he was right,
I knew he was wrong!

We hated one another.
The afternoon turned black.
Then suddenly my brother
Thumped me on the back,
And said, "Oh, *come* along!
We can't go on all night—
I was in the wrong."
So he was in the right.

Portrait By A Neighbour

Edna St. Vincent Millay

Before she has her floor swept
   Or her dishes done,
Any day you'll find her
   A-sunning in the sun!

It's long after midnight
   Her key's in the lock,
And you never see her chimney smoke
   Till past ten o'clock!

She digs in her garden
   With a shovel and a spoon,
She weeds her lazy lettuce
   By the light of the moon,

She walks up the walk
   Like a woman in a dream,
She forgets she borrowed butter
   And pays you back cream!

Her lawn looks like a meadow,
   And if she mows the place
She leaves the clover standing
   And the Queen Anne's lace!

Some People

Rachel Field

Isn't it strange some people make
    You feel so tired inside,
Your thoughts begin to shrivel up
    Like leaves all brown and dried!

But when you're with some other ones,
    It's stranger still to find
Your thoughts as thick as fireflies
    All shining in your mind!

The Cowboy's Life

Attributed to James Barton Adams

The bawl of a steer
To a cowboy's ear,
Is music of sweetest strain;
And the yelping notes
Of the gay coyotes
To him are a glad refrain.

For a kingly crown
In the noisy town
His saddle he wouldn't change;
No life so free
As the life we see
Way out on the Yaso range.

The rapid beat
Of his bronco's feet
On the sod as he speeds along,
Keeps living time
To the ringing rhyme
Of his rollicking cowboy song.

The winds may blow
And the thunder growl
Or the breezes may safely moan;—
A cowboy's life
Is a royal life,
His saddle his kingly throne.

Lincoln

Nancy Byrd Turner

There was a boy of other days,
A quiet, awkward, earnest lad,
Who trudged long weary miles to get
A book on which his heart was set—
And then no candle had!

He was too poor to buy a lamp
But very wise in woodmen's ways.
He gathered seasoned bough and stem,
And crisping leaf, and kindled them
Into a ruddy blaze.

Then as he lay full length and read,
The firelight flickered on his face,
And etched his shadow on the gloom.
And made a picture in the room,
In that most humble place.

The hard years came, the hard years went,
But, gentle, brave, and strong of will
He met them all. And when to-day
We see his pictured face, we say,
"There's light upon it still."

A Baby's Feet

Algernon Charles Swinburne

A baby's feet, like sea-shells pink,
  Might tempt, should heaven see meet
An angel's lips to kiss, we think,
  A baby's feet

Like rose-hued sea-flowers toward the heat
  They stretch and spread and wink
Their ten soft buds that part and meet.

No flower-bells that expand and shrink
  Gleam half so heavenly sweet,
As shine on life's untrodden brink
  A baby's feet.

my friend

Emily Hearn

my friend is
like bark
rounding a tree

he warms
like sun
on a winter day

he cools
like water
in the hot noon

his voice
is ready
as a spring bird

he is
my friend
and I
am his

You Are Old, Father William

Lewis Carroll
(Charles Lutwidge Dodgson)

'You are old, Father William,' the young man said,
   'And your hair has become very white;
And yet you incessantly stand on your head—
   Do you think, at your age, it is right?'

'In my youth,' Father William replied to his son,
   'I feared it might injure the brain;
But, now that I'm perfectly sure I have none,
   Why, I do it again and again.'

'You are old,' said the youth, 'as I mentioned before,
   And have grown most uncommonly fat;
Yet you turned a back-somersault in at the door—
   Pray, what is the reason of that?'

'In my youth,' said the sage, as he shook his grey locks,
   'I kept all my limbs very supple
By the use of this ointment—one shilling the box—
   Allow me to sell you a couple?'

'You are old,' said the youth, 'and your jaws are too weak
   For anything tougher than suet;
Yet you finished the goose, with the bones and the beak—
   Pray, how did you manage to do it?'

Little Puppy

From The Navajo American Indian
Transcribed by Hilda Faunce Wetherill

Little puppy with the black spots,
Come and herd the flock with me.
We will climb the red rocks
And from the top we'll see
The tall cliffs, the straight cliffs,
The fluted cliffs,
Where the eagles live.
We'll see the dark rocks,
The smooth rocks,
That hold the rain to give us
Water, when we eat our bread and meat,
When the sun is high.
Little spotted dog of mine,
Come and spend the day with me.
When the sun is going down
Behind the pointed hill,
We will follow home the flock
They will lead the way
To the hogans where the fires burn
And the square cornbread is in the ashes,
Waiting our return.

Snake woman

Margaret Atwood

I was once the snake woman,

the only person, it seems, in the whole place
who wasn't terrified of them.

I used to hunt with two sticks
among milkweed and under porches and logs
for this vein of cool green metal
which would run through my fingers like mercury
or turn to a raw bracelet
gripping my wrist:

I could follow them by their odour,
a sick smell, acid and glandular,
part skunk, part inside
of a torn stomach,
the smell of their fear.

Once caught, I'd carry them,
limp and terrorized, into the dining room,
something even men were afraid of.
What fun I had!
Put that thing in my bed and I'll kill you.

Now, I don't know.
Now I'd consider the snake.

THOUGHTS AND FEELINGS

Illustrated by
Chi Chung

Anxious
Miriam Waddington

Anxious
of course I'm anxious
afraid
of course I'm afraid
I don't know what about
I don't know what of
but I'm afraid
and I feel it's
right to be.

Orders
A.M. *Klein*

Muffle the wind;
Silence the clock;
Muzzle the mice;
Curb the small talk;
Cure the hinge-squeak;
Banish the thunder.
Let me sit silent,
Let me wonder.

Books Fall Open

David McCord

Books fall open,
you fall in,
delighted where
you've never been;
hear voices not once
heard before,
reach world on world
through door on door;
find unexpected
keys to things
looked up beyond
imaginings.
What *might* you be,
perhaps *become*,
because one book
is somewhere? Some
wise delver into
wisdom, wit,
and wherewithal
has written it.

Little

Dorothy Aldis

I am the sister of him
   And he is my brother.
He is too little for us
   To talk to each other.

So every morning I show him
   My doll and my book;
But every morning he still is
   Too little to look

Chocolate Cake

Jack Prelutsky

I am lying in the darkness
with a smile upon my face,
as I'm thinking of my stomach,
which has got an empty space,
and that corner of the kitchen
with the piece of chocolate cake
I have got to get my hands on
for my empty stomach's sake.

When my parents both are sleeping
(I can tell by Father's snore),
I will sneak out of my bedroom,
I will tiptoe past their door,
I will slip into the kitchen
without any noise or light,
and if I'm really careful,
I will have that cake tonight.

The Land Of Story Books

Robert Louis Stevenson

At evening when the lamp is lit,
Around the fire my parents sit;
They sit at home and talk and sing,
And do not play at anything.

Now, with my little gun, I crawl
All in the dark along the wall,
And follow round the forest track
Away behind the sofa back.

There, in the night, where none can spy,
All in my hunter's camp I lie,
And play at books that I have read
Till it is time to go to bed.

These are the hills, these are the woods,
These are my starry solitudes;
And there the river by whose brink
The roaring lions come to drink.

I see the others far away
As if in firelit camp they lay,
And I, like to an Indian scout,
Around their party prowled about.

So, when my nurse comes in for me,
Home I return across the sea,
And go to bed with backward looks
At my dear Land of Story Books.

illustrated on cover

43

Me

Walter de la Mare

As long as I live
I shall always be
My Self—and no other,
Just me.

Like a tree—
Willow, elder,
Aspen, thorn,
Or cypress forlorn.

Like a flower,
For its hour—
Primrose, or pink,
Or a violet—
Sunned by the sun,
And with dewdrops wet.

Always just me.
Till the day come on
When I leave this body,
It's all then done,
And the spirit within it
Is gone.

I Like It When It's Mizzly

Aileen Fisher

I like it when it's mizzly
and just a little drizzly
so everything looks far away
and make-believe and frizzly.

I like it when it's foggy
and sounding very froggy.
I even like it when it rains
on streets and weepy windowpanes
and catkins in the poplar tree
and *me*.

Skipping Along Alone

Winifred Welles

Oh, how I love to skip alone
    Along the beach in moisty weather;
The whole world seems my very own,
Each fluted shell and glistening stone,
    Each wave that twirls a silver feather.

I skip along so brave and big
    Behind the sand-birds gray and tiny,

I love to see their quick feet jig,
Each leaves a mark, neat as a twig,
   Stamped in the sand so clear and shiny.

And fine and faint as drops of spray
   I hear their little voices calling,
"Sweet, sweet! Sweet, sweet!" I hear them say—
I love to skip alone and play
   Along the sand when mist is falling.

A Song Of Greatness

A Chippewa Indian song
Transcribed by Mary Austin

When I hear the old men
Telling of heroes,
Telling of great deeds
Of ancient days,
When I hear them telling,
Then I think within me
I too am one of these.

When I hear the people
Praising great ones,
Then I know that I too
Shall be esteemed,
I too when my time comes
Shall do mightily.

Beauty

Beauty is seen
In the sunlight,
The trees, the birds,
Corn growing and people working
Or dancing for their harvest.

Beauty is heard
In the night,
Wind sighing, rain falling,
Or a singer chanting
Anything in earnest.

Beauty is in yourself.
Good deeds, happy thoughts

Wisdom

Langston Hughes

I stand most humbly
Before man's wisdom
Knowing we are not
Really wise:

If we were
We'd open up the kingdom
And make earth happy
As the dreamed of skies.

50

Leisure

William Henry Davies

What is this life if, full of care,
We have no time to stand and stare.

No time to stand beneath the boughs
And stare as long as sheep or cows.

No time to see, when woods we pass,
Where squirrels hide their nuts in grass.

No time to see, in broad daylight,
Streams full of stars, like stars at night.

No time to turn at Beauty's glance,
And watch her feet, how they can dance.

No time to wait till her mouth can
Enrich that smile her eyes began.

A poor life this if, full of care,
We have no time to stand and stare.

You better be ready

John Lane

What are all those rocks sticking up for? he says.
Those are markers for graves.
Graves?
Where they bury people, after you die.
No, you are wrong, Uncle Johnny. When you die, God
    takes you away in a car.
Whereabouts?
Whereabouts?
Yes. Whereabouts does God take you?
It's a secret, he says.
Well, there are people buried right there!
I know, Uncle Johnny. But they just missed their ride,
    that's all.
Oh, I say.

Stopping By Woods On A Snowy Evening

Robert Frost

Whose woods these are I think I know.
His house is in the village though;
He will not see me stopping here
To watch his woods fill up with snow.

My little horse must think it queer
To stop without a farmhouse near
Between the woods and frozen lake
The darkest evening of the year.

He gives his harness bells a shake
To ask if there is some mistake.
The only other sound's the sweep
Of easy wind and downy flake.

The woods are lovely, dark and deep.
But I have promises to keep,
And miles to go before I sleep,
And miles to go before I sleep.

in Just-

E.E. *Cummings*

in Just-
spring   when the world is mud-
luscious the little
lame balloonman

whistles   far   and wee

and eddieandbill come
running from marbles and
piracies and it's
spring

when the world is puddle-wonderful

the queer
old balloonman whistles
far   and   wee
and bettyandisbel come dancing

from hop-scotch and jump-rope and

it's
spring
and
     the
             goat-footed

balloonMan   whistles
far
and
wee

This book was set in Novarese
and composed by Marjorie Campolongo
It was printed on 50 lb. Finch Opaque.
title page illustration by Tony DeLuna

Editor: Deborah Jerome-Cohen
Design: Patricia Isaza

Permissions: